Bond

Non-verbal Reasoning
Assessment Papers

8–9 years

Andrew Baines

Nelson Thornes

First published in 2003 by:
Nelson Thornes Ltd

This edition published in 2011 by:
Nelson Thornes Ltd
Delta Place
27 Bath Road
CHELTENHAM
GL53 7TH
United Kingdom

13 / 2

A catalogue record for this book is available from the British Library

ISBN 978 1 4085 1626 3

Illustrations by Nigel Kitching
Page make-up by Wearset Ltd

Printed in China by 1010 Printing International Ltd

What is Bond?

This book is part of the Bond Assessment Papers series for non-verbal reasoning, which provides a **thorough and continuous course in non-verbal reasoning** from ages six to twelve. It builds up non-verbal reasoning skills from book to book over the course of the series.

What does this book cover?

Non-verbal reasoning questions can be grouped into four distinct groups: identifying shapes, missing shapes, rotating shapes, coded shapes and logic. This book develops an understanding of these groups through practice of seven different question types: finding the odd one out, completing a visual sequence, completing a shape, completing a visual analogy, reflections, hidden shapes and coded shapes. The questions at this level employ a mixture of pictures and pure shapes. From the next book on, the questions will only involve shapes.

The age given on the cover is for guidance only. As the papers are designed to be reasonably challenging for the age group, any one child may naturally find him or herself working above or below the stated age. The important thing is that children are always encouraged by their performance. Working at the right level is the key to this.

What does the book contain?

- **6 papers** – each one contains 48 questions.

- **Scoring devices** – there is a scoring box at the end of each test and a Progress Chart at the back. The chart is a visual and motivating way for children to see how they are doing. Encouraging them to colour in the chart as they go along and to try to beat their last score can be highly effective!

- **Next Steps** – advice on what to do after finishing the papers can be found on the inside back cover.

- **Answers** – located in an easily-removed central pull-out section.

How can you use this book?

One of the great strengths of Bond Assessment Papers is their flexibility. They can be used at home, school and by tutors to:

- provide regular non-verbal reasoning practice in **bite-sized chunks**
- **highlight strengths and weaknesses** in the core skills
- identify **individual needs**
- set **homework**
- set **timed formal practice** tests – allow about 35 minutes.

It is best to start at the beginning and work through the papers in order.

What does a score mean and how can it be improved?

If children colour in the Progress Chart at the back, this will give an idea of how they are doing. The Next Steps inside the back cover will help you to decide what to do next to help a child progress. We suggest that it is always valuable to go over any wrong answers with children.

Don't forget the website . . . !

Visit www.bond11plus.co.uk for lots of advice, information and suggestions on everything to do with Bond, helping children to do their best, and exams.

Paper 1

Which is the odd one out? Circle the letter.

Example

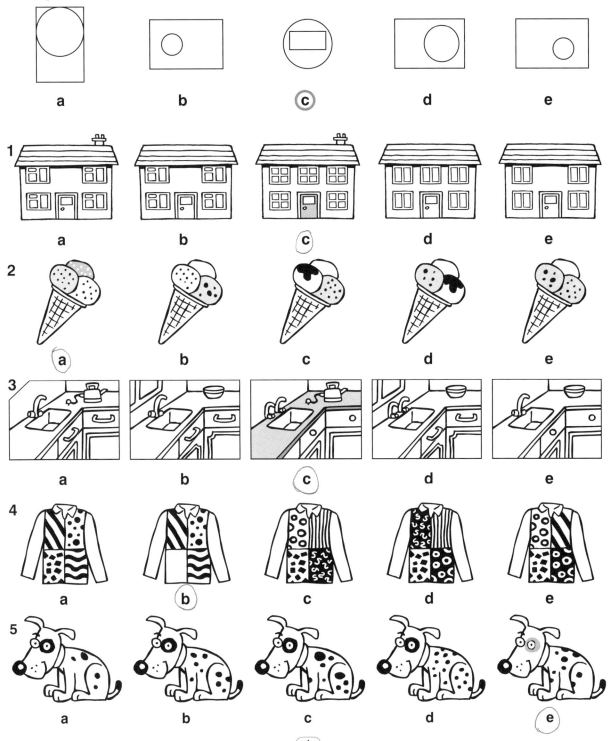

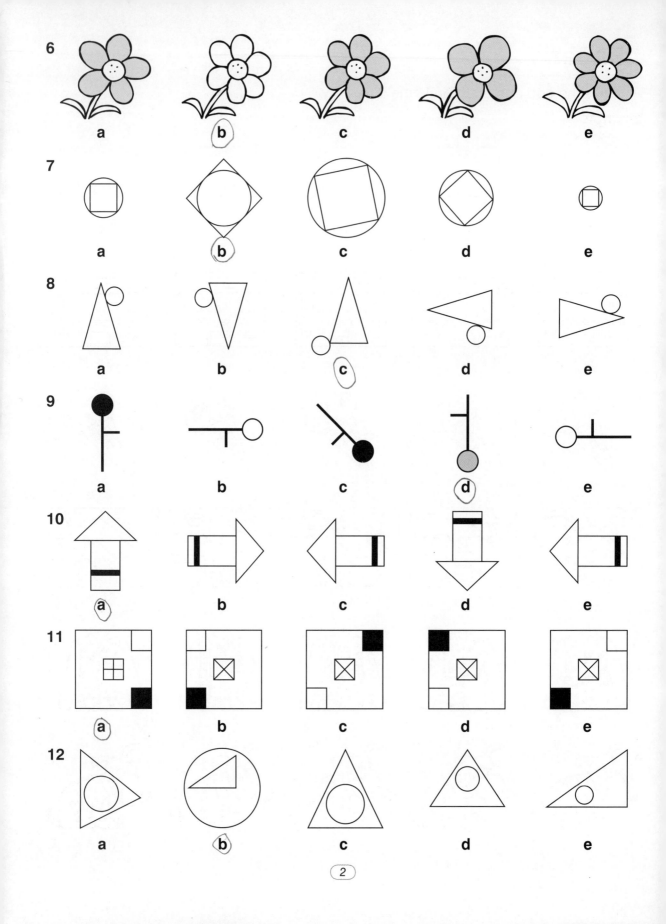

6   a   b   c   d   e

7   a   b   c   d   e

8   a   b   c   d   e

9   a   b   c   d   e

10   a   b   c   d   e

11   a   b   c   d   e

12   a   b   c   d   e

Which one comes next? Circle the letter.

Example

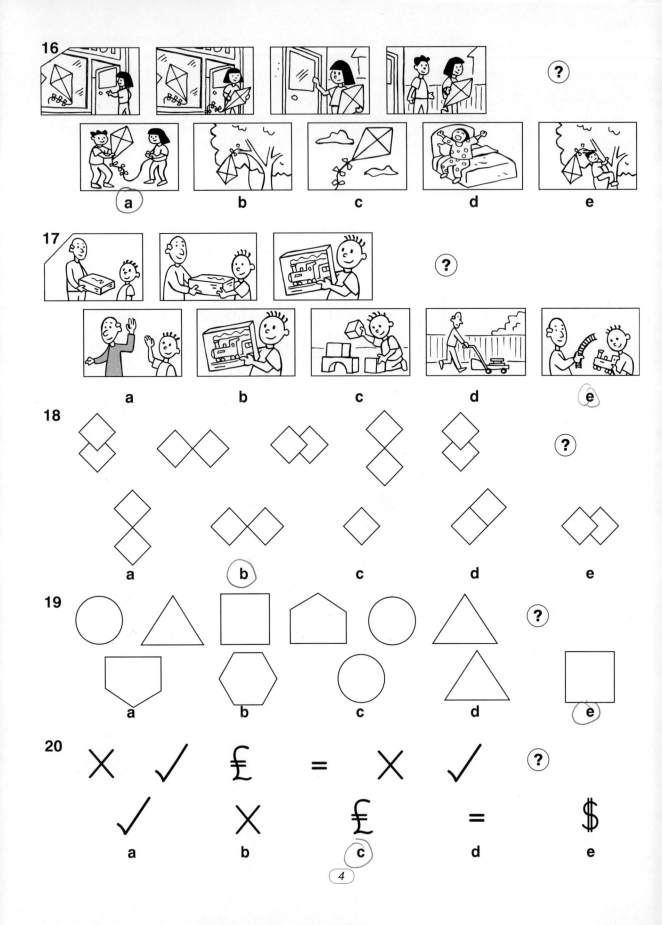

16

a b c d e

17

a b c d e

18

a b c d e

19

a b c d e

20

a b c d e

4

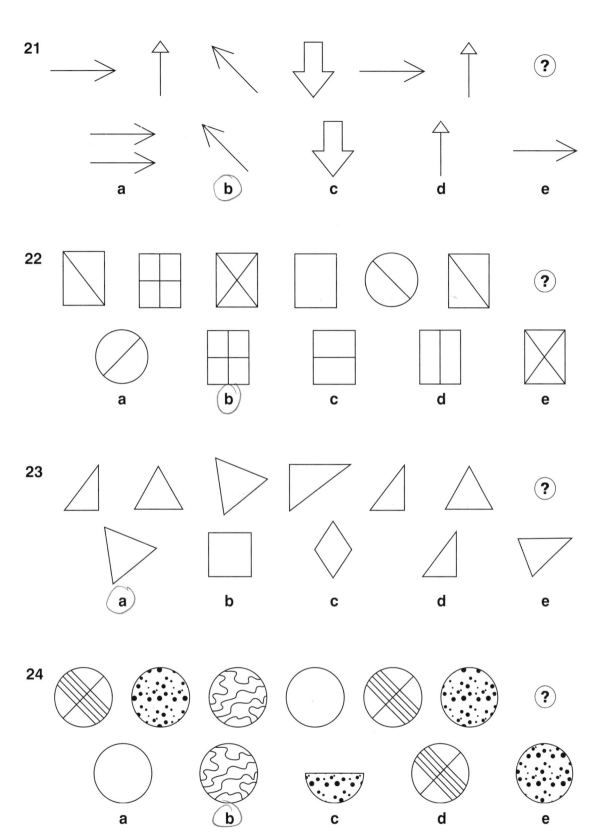

Which picture completes the second pair in the same way as the first pair?
Circle the letter.

Example

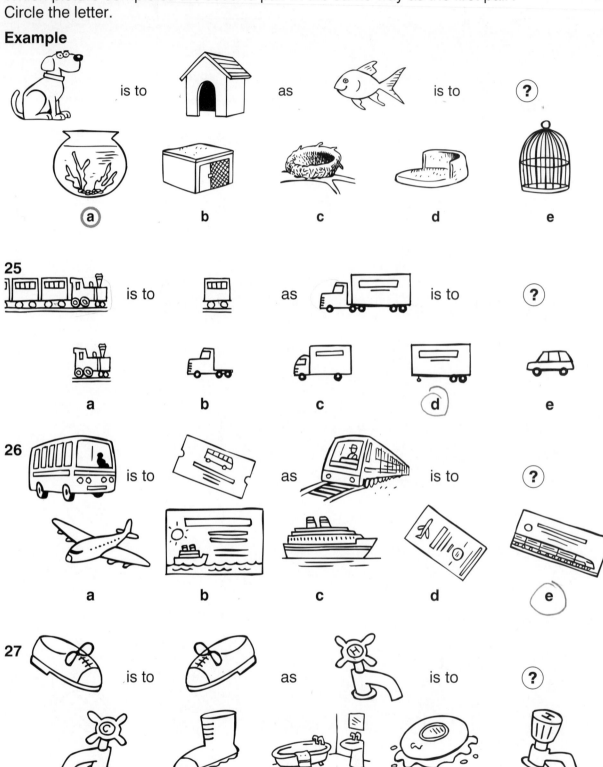

25

26

27

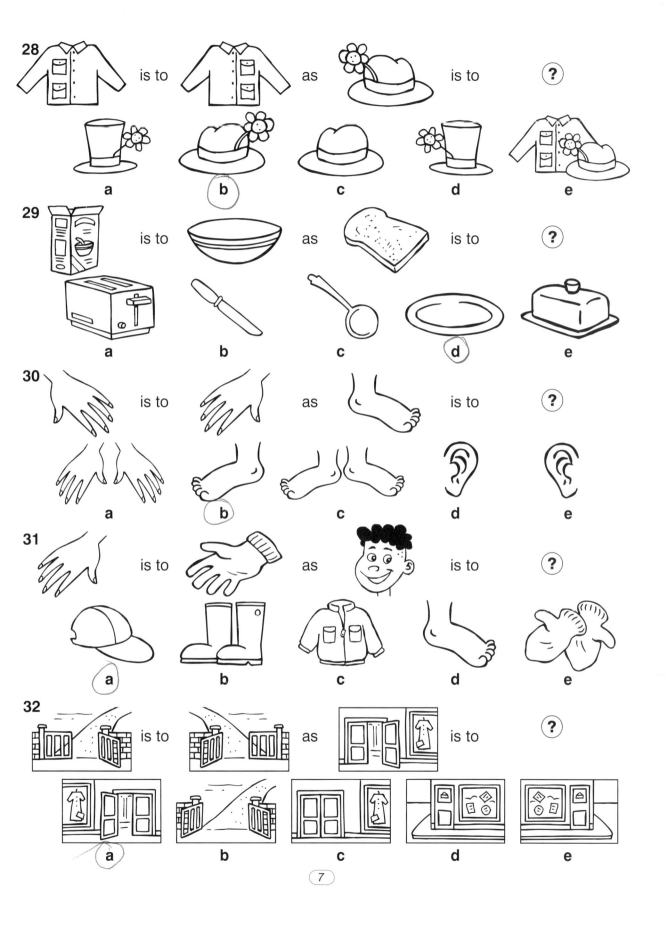

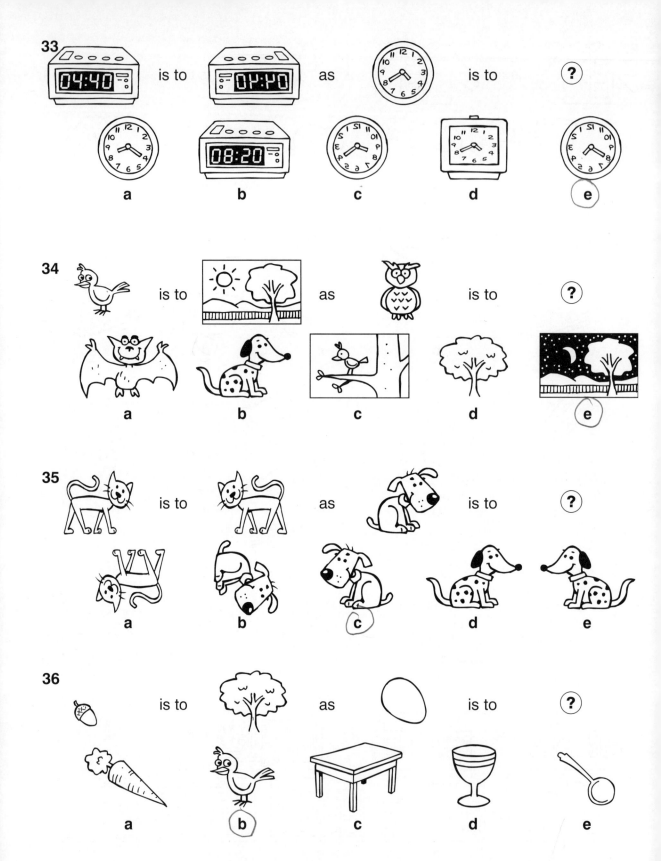

33

34

35

36

In which larger picture is the smaller picture hidden? Circle the letter.

Example

Which shape or picture completes the larger square? Circle the letter.

Example

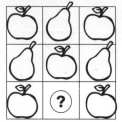

a

b

ⓒ

d

e

43

ⓐ

b

c

d

e

44

a

ⓑ

c

d

e

45

a

b

ⓒ

d

e

46

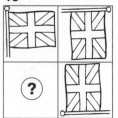

ⓐ

ⓑ

c

d

e

10

47

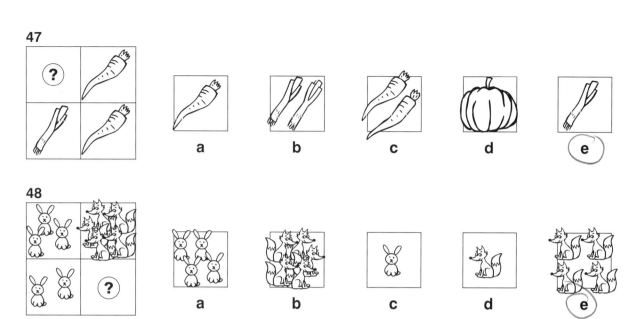

48

Paper 2

Which is the odd one out? Circle the letter.

Example

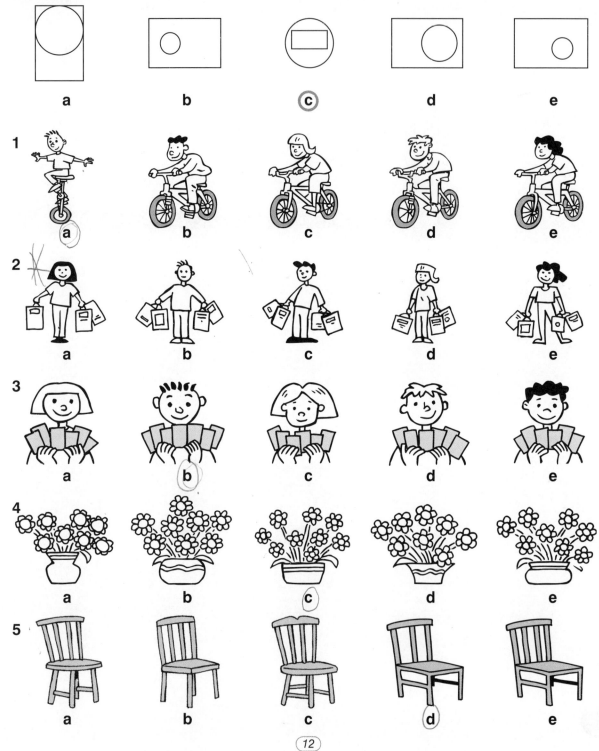

a   b   ⓒ   d   e

1   a   b   c   d   e

2   a   b   c   d   e

3   a   b   c   d   e

4   a   b   c   d   e

5   a   b   c   d   e

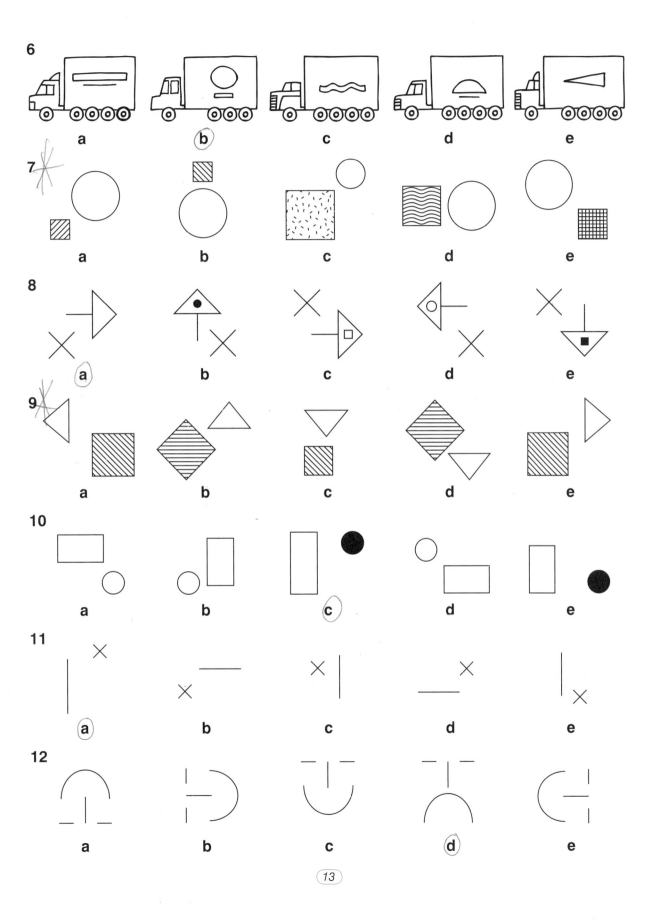

Which one comes next? Circle the letter.

Example

a   b   c   d   e

13

a   b   c   d   e

14

a   b   c   d   e

15

a   b   c   d   e

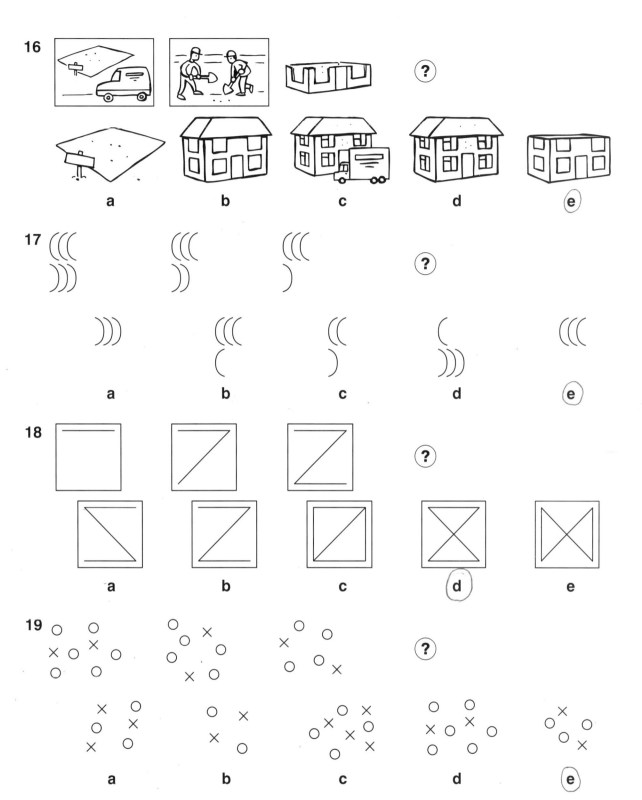

16

a b c d e

17

a b c d e

18

a b c d e

19

a b c d e

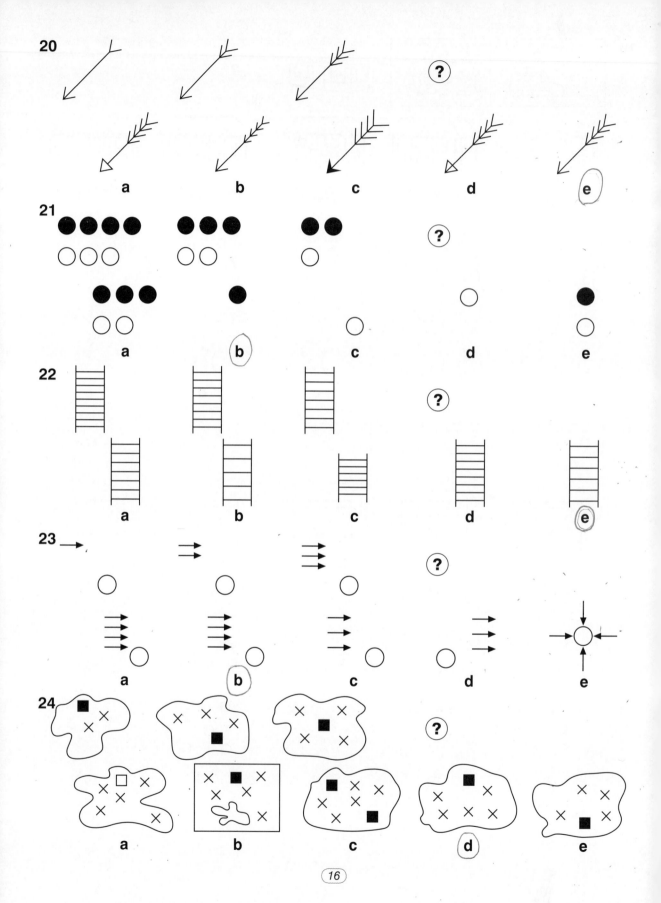

Which shape or pattern completes the second pair in the same way as the first pair?
Circle the letter.

Example

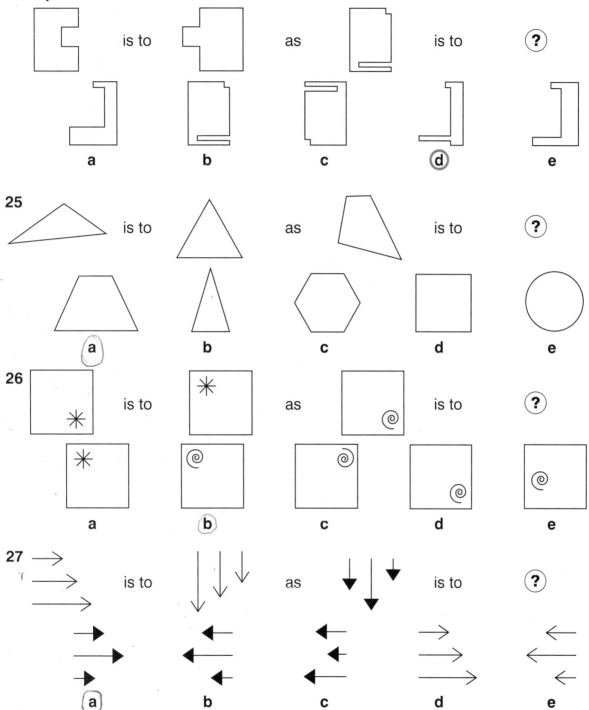

25

26

27

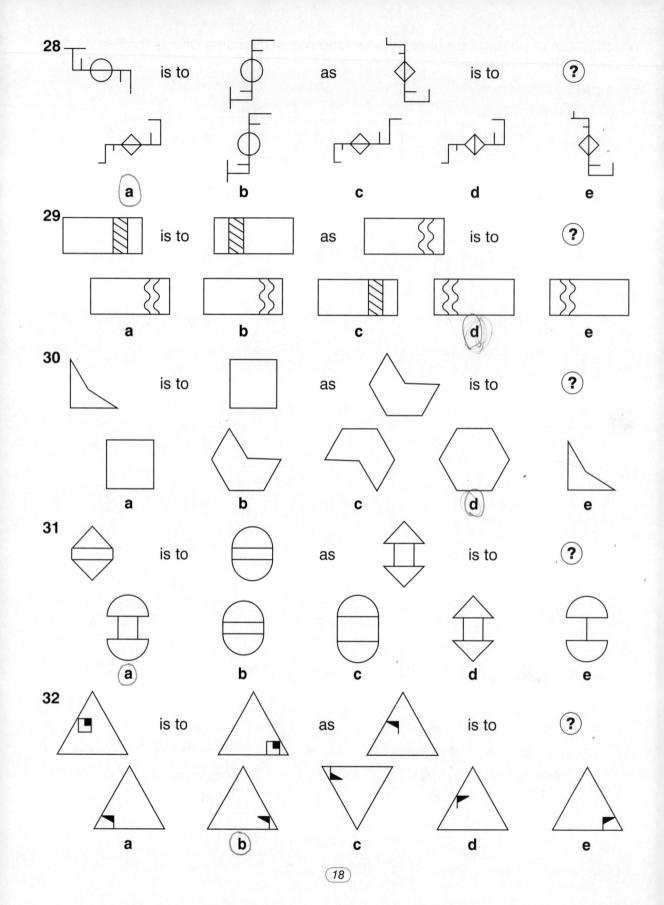

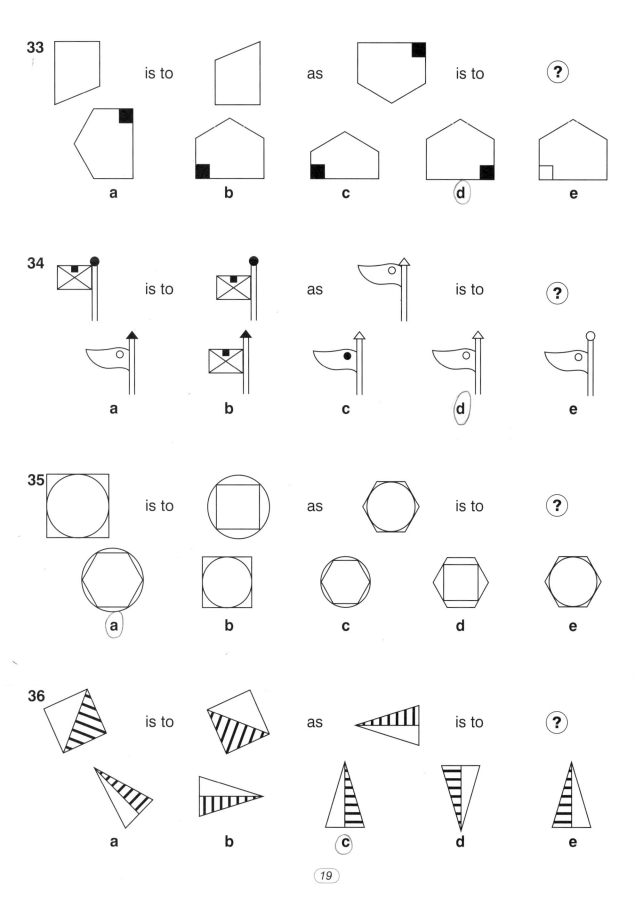

In which larger shape is the shape on the left hidden? Circle the letter.

Example

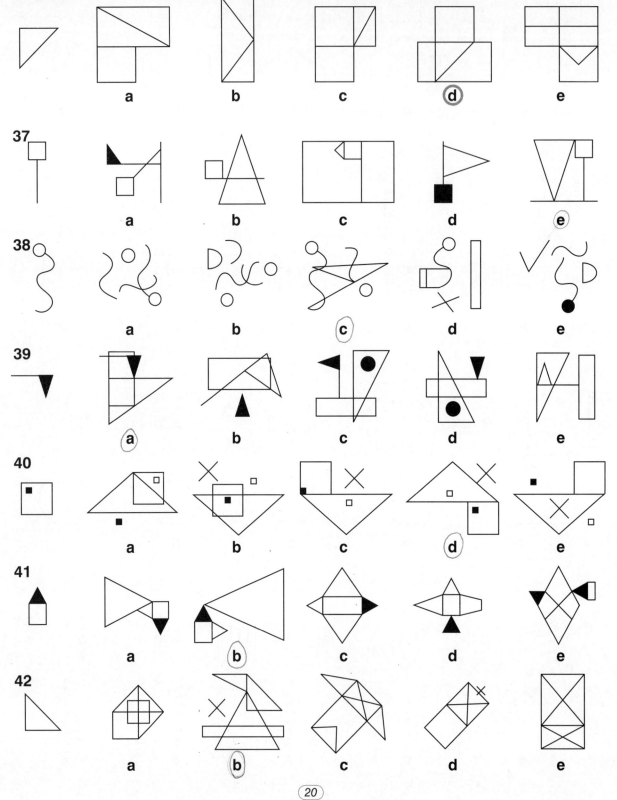

a   b   c   d   e

37

38

39

40

41

42

20

Which picture on the right is the reflection of the picture given on the left, in the dotted mirror line? Circle the letter.

Example

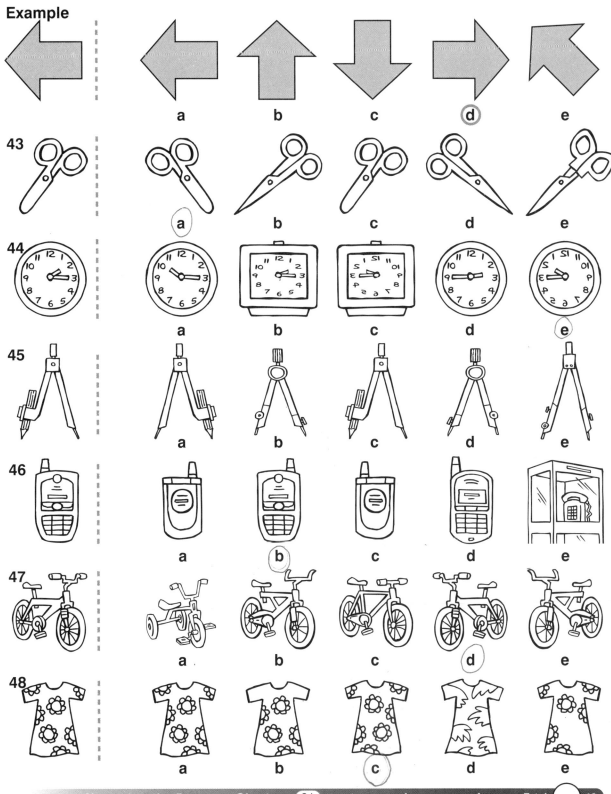

a b c (d) e

43 a b c d e

44 a b c d (e)

45 a b c d e

46 a (b) c d e

47 a b c (d) e

48 a b (c) d e

Paper 3

Which is the odd one out? Circle the letter.

Example

a   b   c   d   e

1

a   b   c   d   e

2

a   b   c   d   e

3

a   b   c   d   e

4

a   b   c   d   e

5

a   b   c   d   e

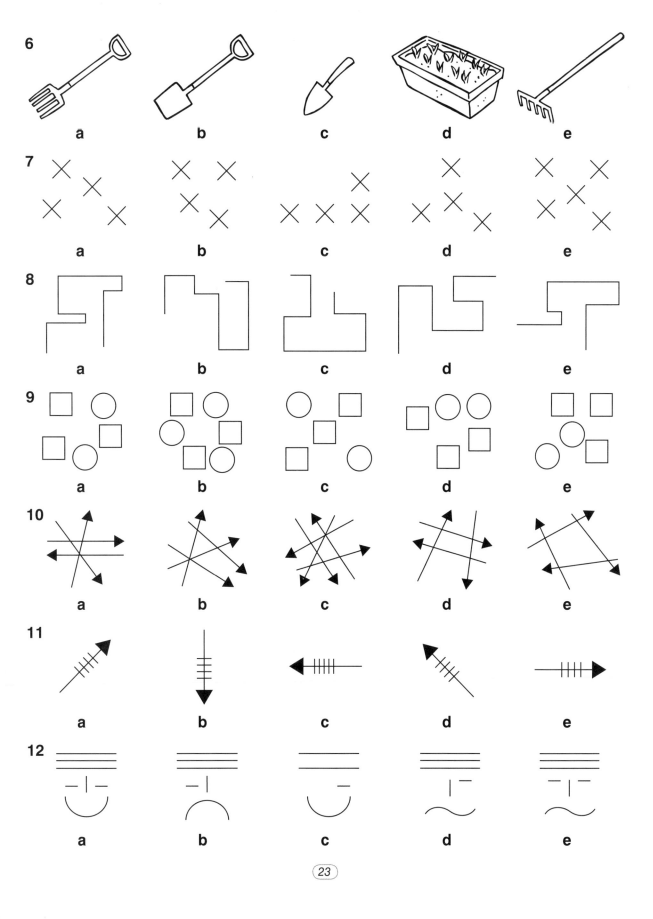

Which one comes next? Circle the letter.

Example

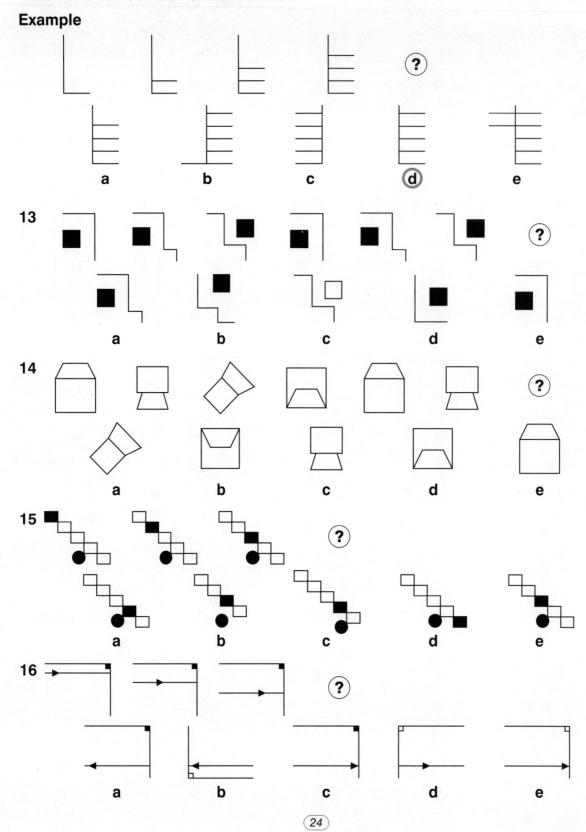

13

14

15

16

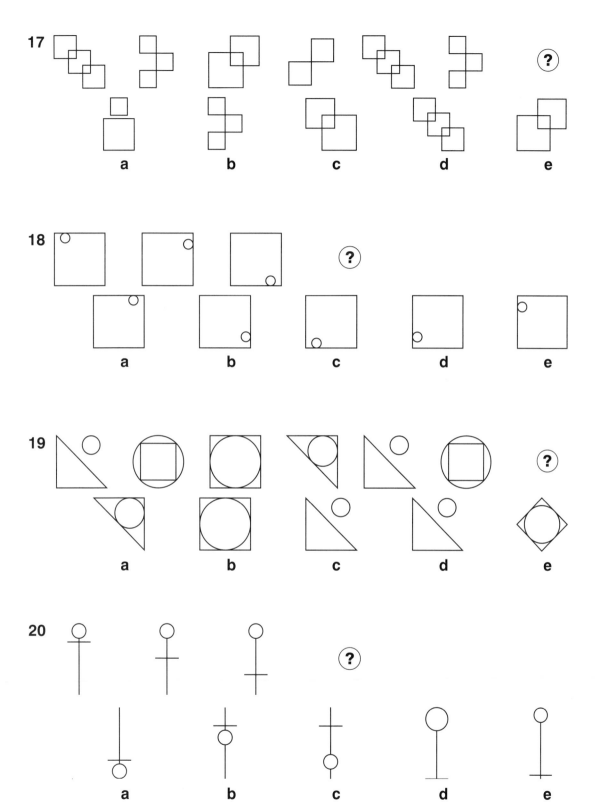

17

a b c d e

18

a b c d e

19

a b c d e

20

a b c d e

25

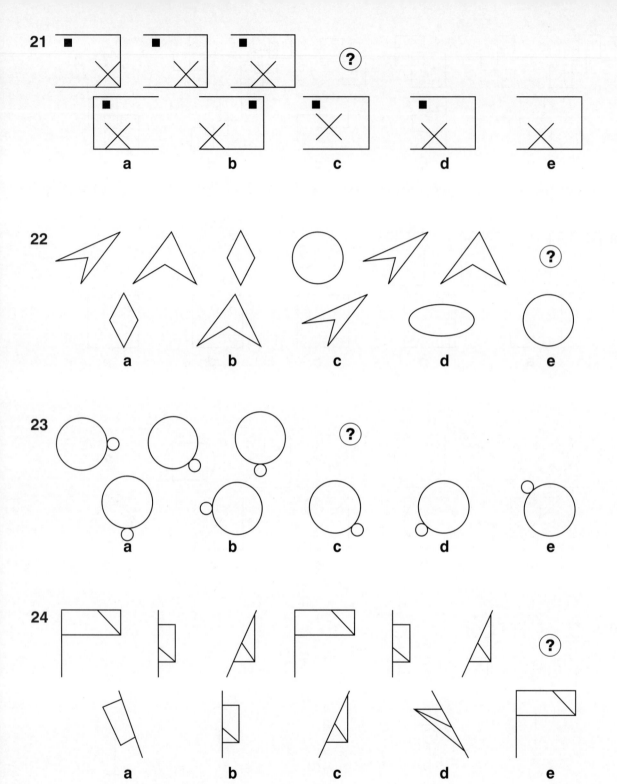

Which picture completes the second pair in the same way as the first pair?
Circle the letter.

Example

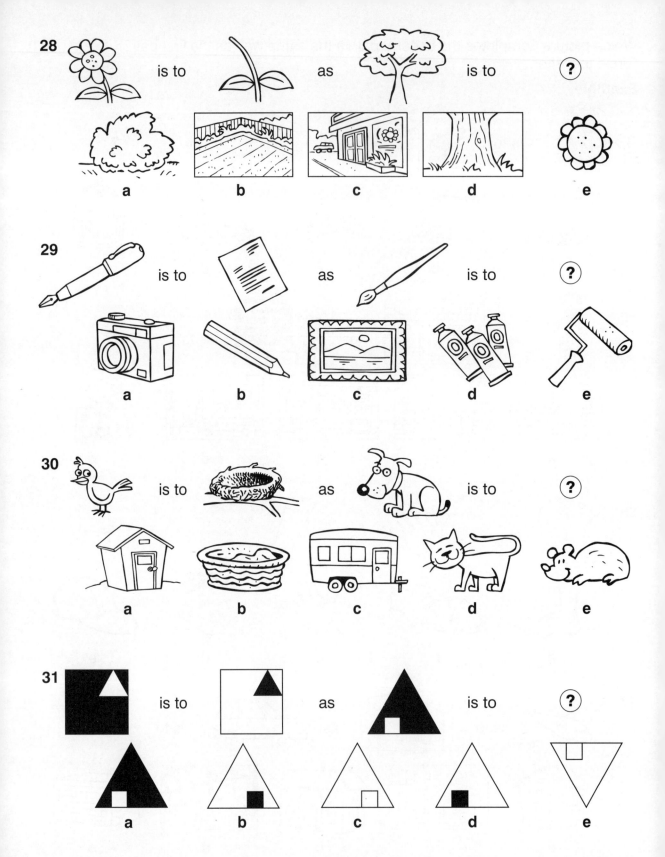

28 is to   as   is to   **?**

a   b   c   d   e

29 is to   as   is to   **?**

a   b   c   d   e

30 is to   as   is to   **?**

a   b   c   d   e

31 is to   as   is to   **?**

a   b   c   d   e

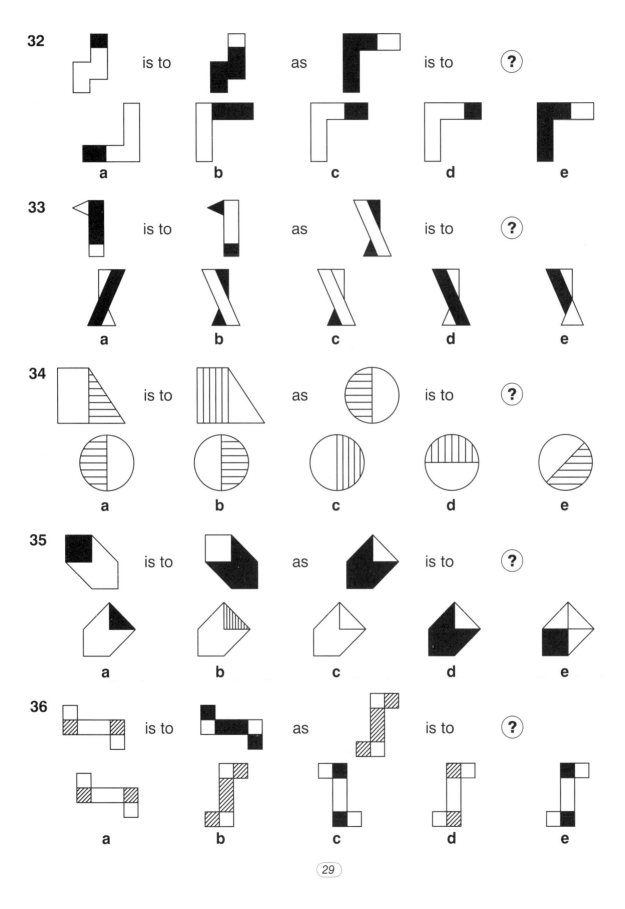

Which shape on the right is the reflection of the shape given on the left?
Circle the letter.

Example

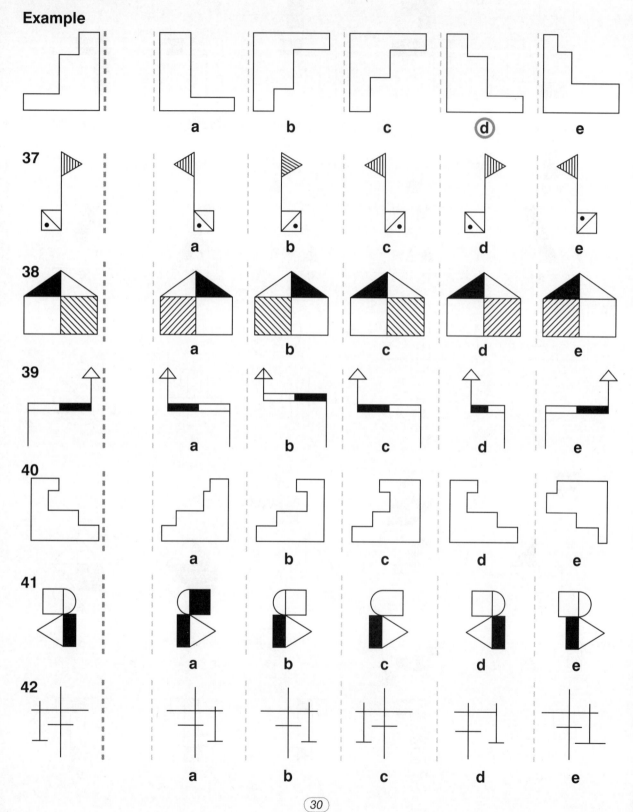

a   b   c   (d)   e

37

a   b   c   d   e

38

a   b   c   d   e

39

a   b   c   d   e

40

a   b   c   d   e

41

a   b   c   d   e

42

a   b   c   d   e

Paper 1

1	c	25	d
2	a	26	e
3	c	27	a
4	b	28	b
5	e	29	d
6	b	30	b
7	b	31	a
8	c	32	a
9	d	33	e
10	a	34	e
11	a	35	c
12	b	36	b
13	d	37	a
14	b	38	b
15	d	39	c
16	a	40	c
17	e	41	a
18	b	42	c
19	e	43	a
20	c	44	b
21	b	45	c
22	b	46	a
23	a	47	e
24	b	48	e

Paper 2

1	a	25	d
2	e	26	b
3	b	27	b
4	c	28	a
5	d	29	d
6	b	30	d
7	c	31	a
8	a	32	b
9	c	33	b
10	c	34	d
11	a	35	c
12	d	36	c
13	c	37	e
14	e	38	c
15	a	39	a
16	e	40	d
17	e	41	b
18	d	42	b
19	e	43	a
20	e	44	e
21	b	45	a
22	e	46	b
23	b	47	d
24	d	48	c

Paper 3

1	e	25	b
2	a	26	a
3	b	27	e
4	d	28	d
5	e	29	c
6	d	30	b
7	e	31	d
8	a	32	c
9	b	33	d
10	c	34	c
11	c	35	a
12	c	36	e
13	e	37	c
14	a	38	a
15	a	39	c
16	c	40	b
17	e	41	b
18	d	42	b
19	b	43	d
20	e	44	e
21	d	45	c
22	a	46	e
23	d	47	b
24	e	48	d

Paper 4

1	a	25	b
2	e	26	c
3	e	27	e
4	c	28	b
5	c	29	b
6	a	30	c
7	b	31	e
8	b	32	a
9	d	33	b
10	e	34	e
11	a	35	a
12	e	36	a
13	c	37	a
14	b	38	a
15	d	39	c
16	c	40	d
17	b	41	e
18	d	42	c
19	a	43	c
20	d	44	b
21	b	45	e
22	d	46	d
23	a	47	d
24	e	48	c

Paper 5

1 e		**25** d	
2 b		**26** d	
3 c		**27** a	
4 b		**28** b	
5 c		**29** b	
6 e		**30** e	
7 a		**31** d	
8 b		**32** e	
9 e		**33** c	
10 d		**34** e	
11 c		**35** d	
12 c		**36** b	
13 e		**37** a	
14 c		**38** d	
15 d		**39** b	
16 d		**40** c	
17 b		**41** d	
18 c		**42** b	
19 d		**43** e	
20 b		**44** b	
21 c		**45** c	
22 e		**46** c	
23 a		**47** a	
24 c		**48** e	

Paper 6

1 a		**25** d	
2 d		**26** b	
3 b		**27** e	
4 d		**28** d	
5 b		**29** c	
6 e		**30** d	
7 e		**31** a	
8 d		**32** c	
9 c		**33** a	
10 d		**34** e	
11 e		**35** c	
12 a		**36** b	
13 d		**37** b	
14 a		**38** d	
15 d		**39** e	
16 e		**40** b	
17 b		**41** d	
18 c		**42** a	
19 c		**43** b	
20 b		**44** d	
21 d		**45** e	
22 c		**46** d	
23 a		**47** a	
24 e		**48** e	

ANSWERS

Which code matches the shape or pattern given at the end of each line. Circle the letter.

Example

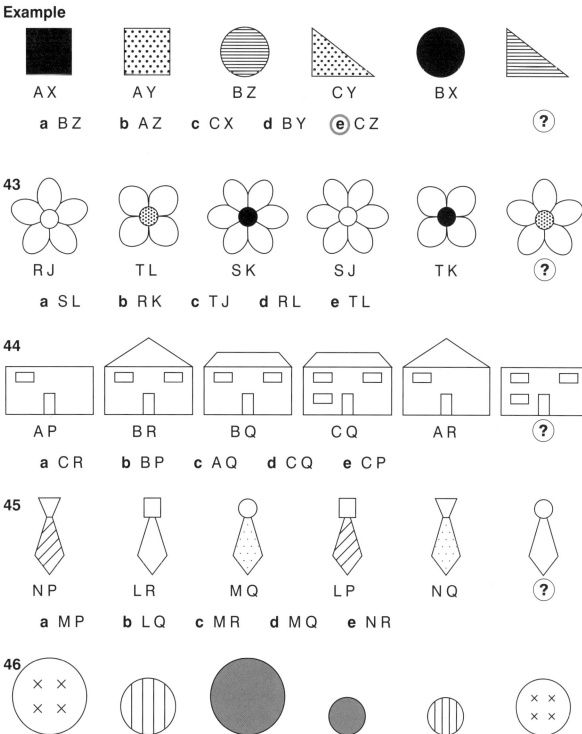

A X   A Y   B Z   C Y   B X

a B Z   **b** A Z   **c** C X   **d** B Y   **(e)** C Z

43

R J   T L   S K   S J   T K

a S L   **b** R K   **c** T J   **d** R L   **e** T L

44

A P   B R   B Q   C Q   A R

a C R   **b** B P   **c** A Q   **d** C Q   **e** C P

45

N P   L R   M Q   L P   N Q

a M P   **b** L Q   **c** M R   **d** M Q   **e** N R

46

H Z   G Y   H X   F X   F Y

a H Z   **b** G X   **c** F Z   **d** H Y   **e** G Z

47

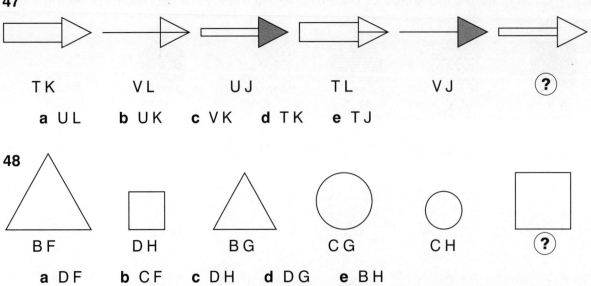

TK   VL   UJ   TL   VJ   (?)

a U L   **b** U K   **c** V K   **d** T K   **e** T J

48

BF   DH   BG   CG   CH   (?)

a D F   **b** C F   **c** D H   **d** D G   **e** B H

Now go to the Progress Chart to record your score!   Total   48

Paper 4

Which is the odd one out? Circle the letter.

Example

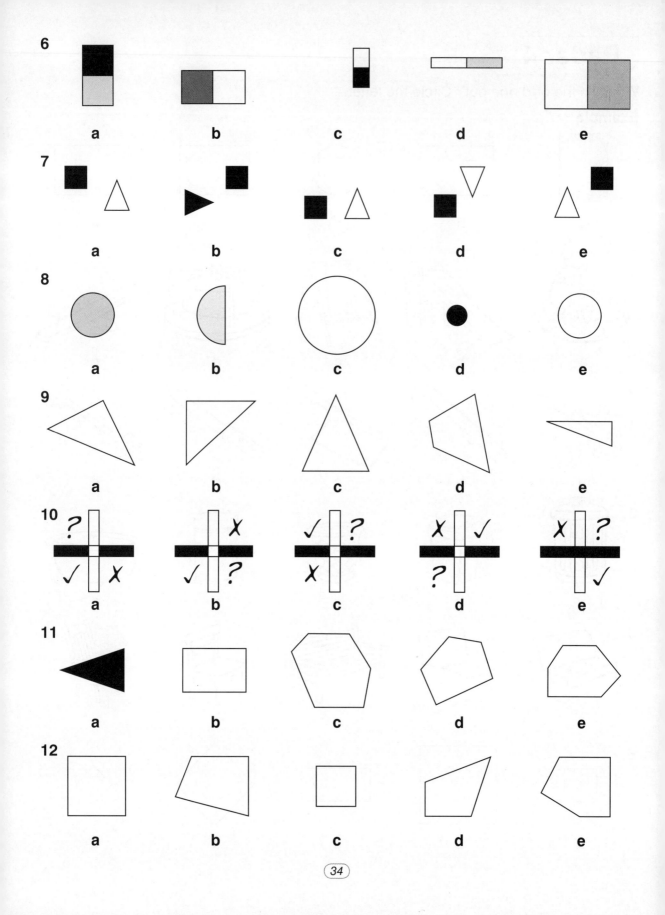

Which one comes next? Circle the letter.

Example

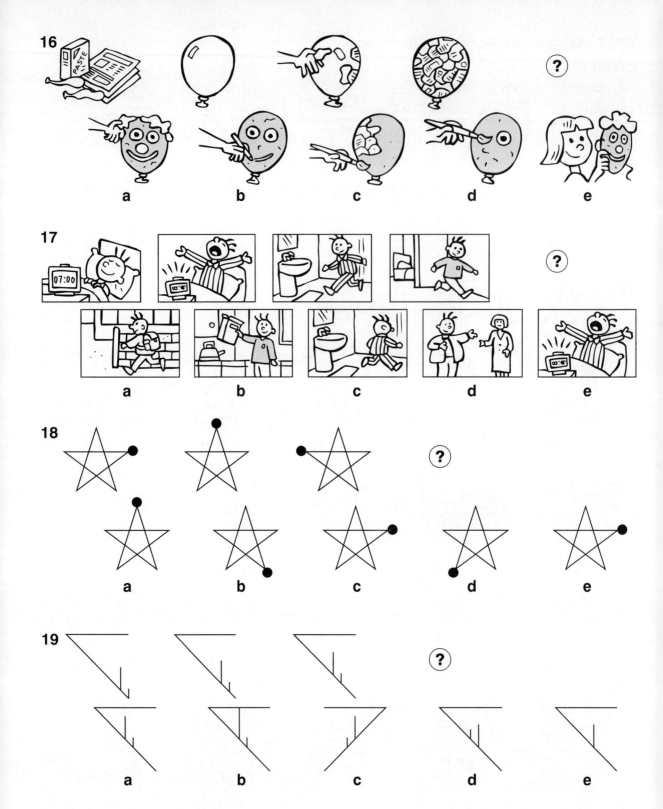

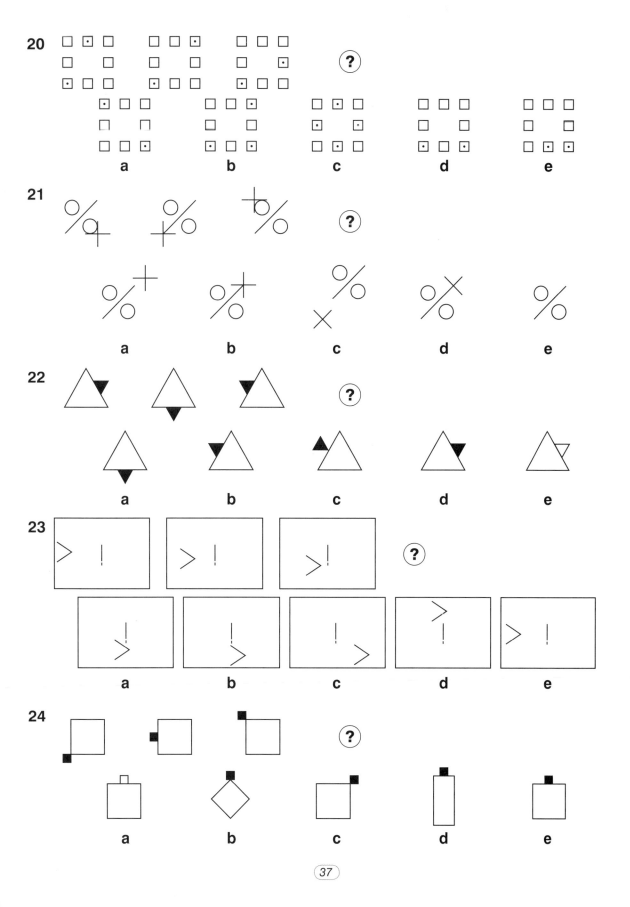

Which shape or pattern on the right completes the second pair in the same way as the first pair? Circle the letter.

Example

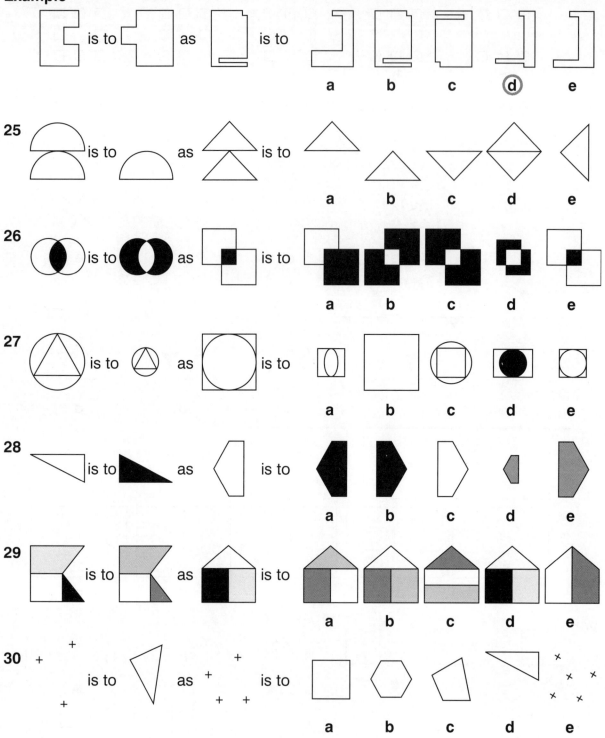

25

26

27

28

29

30

31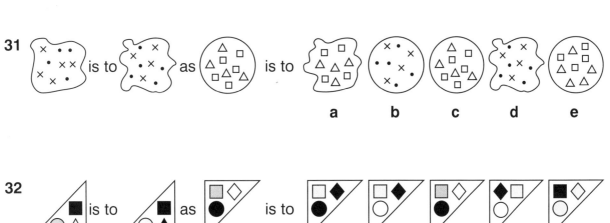

32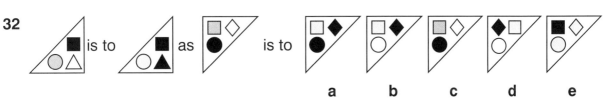

33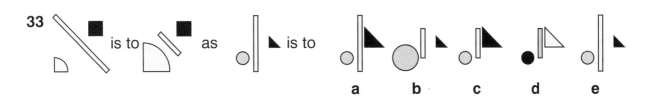

34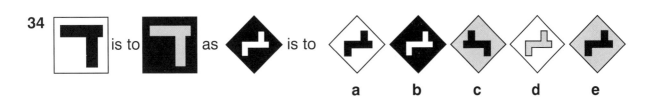

35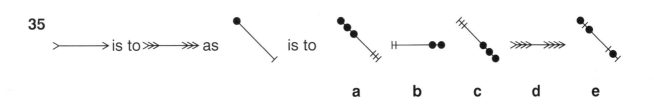

36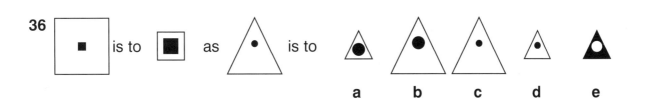

Which shape or pattern completes the larger square? Circle the letter.

Example

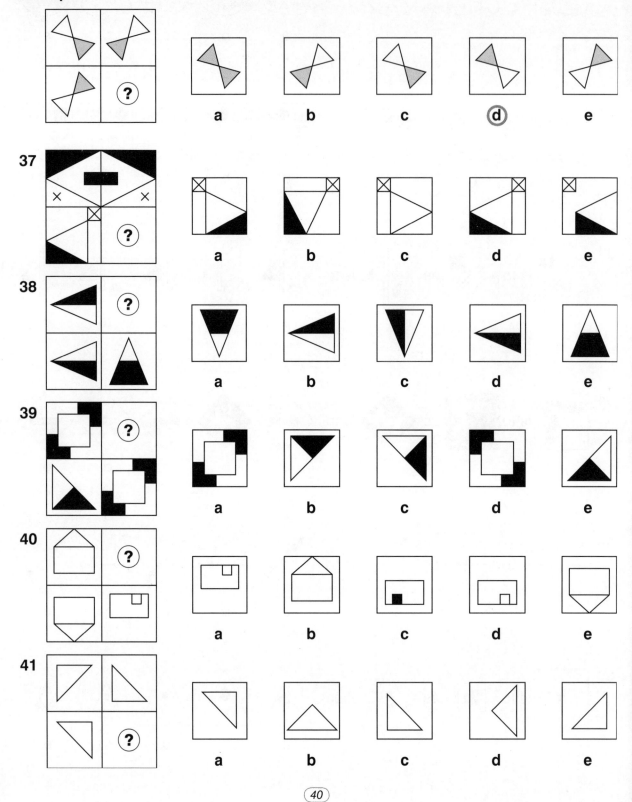

42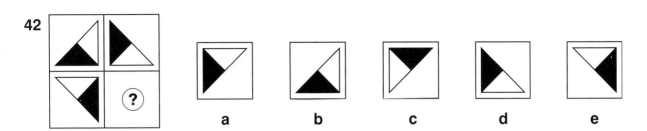

Which code matches the shape or pattern given at the end of each line?
Circle the letter.

Example

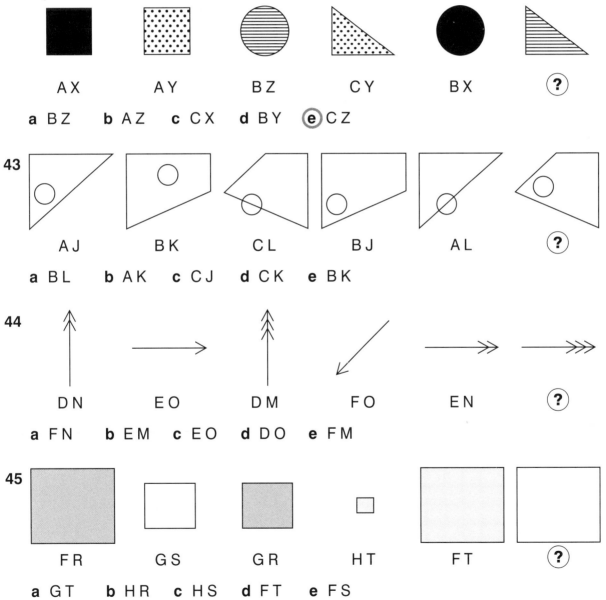

AX   AY   BZ   CY   BX   ?

a BZ   **b** AZ   **c** CX   **d** BY   **e** CZ

43

AJ   BK   CL   BJ   AL   ?

a BL   **b** AK   **c** CJ   **d** CK   **e** BK

44

DN   EO   DM   FO   EN   ?

a FN   **b** EM   **c** EO   **d** DO   **e** FM

45

FR   GS   GR   HT   FT   ?

a GT   **b** HR   **c** HS   **d** FT   **e** FS

46

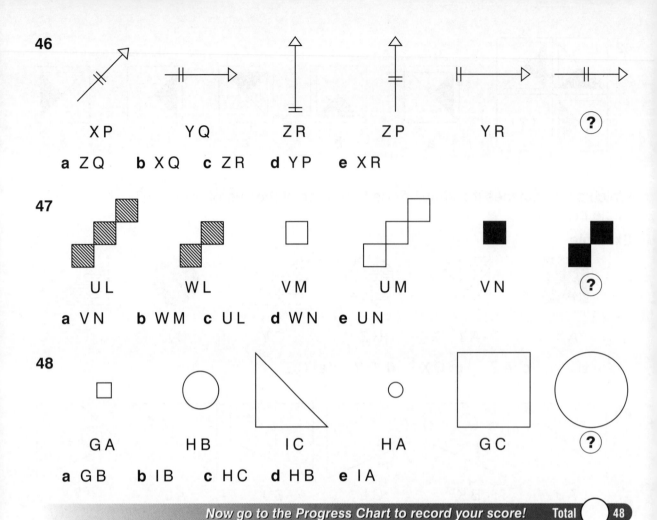

| X P | Y Q | Z R | Z P | Y R | ? |

a Z Q **b** X Q **c** Z R **d** Y P **e** X R

47

| U L | W L | V M | U M | V N | ? |

a V N **b** W M **c** U L **d** W N **e** U N

48

| G A | H B | I C | H A | G C | ? |

a G B **b** I B **c** H C **d** H B **e** I A

Now go to the Progress Chart to record your score!   Total   48

42

Paper 5

Which is the odd one out? Circle the letter.

Example

| a | b | c | d | e |

1

| a | b | c | d | e |

2

| a | b | c | d | e |

3

| a | b | c | d | e |

4

| a | b | c | d | e |

5

| a | b | c | d | e |

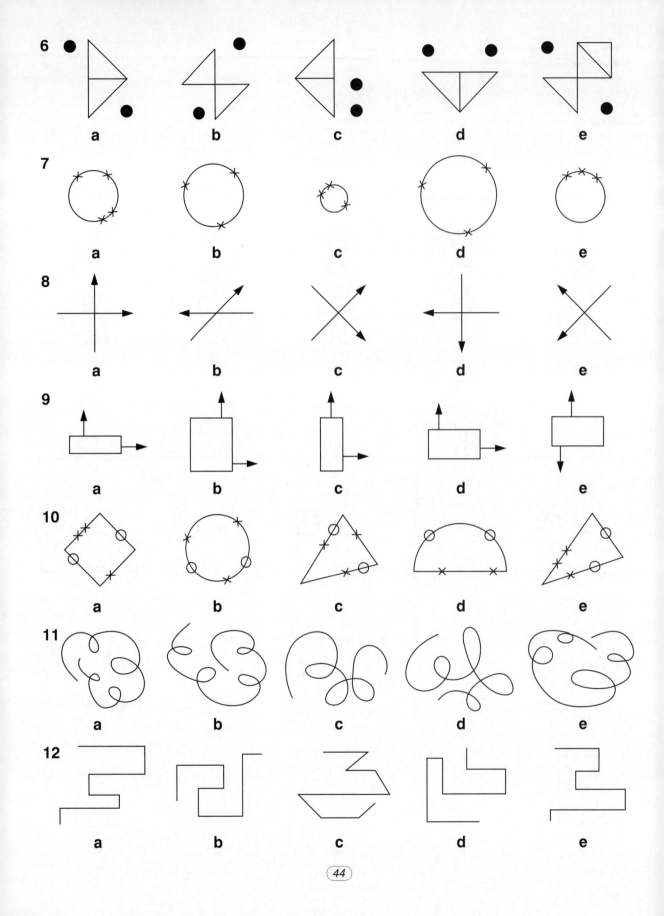

Which one comes next? Circle the letter.

Example

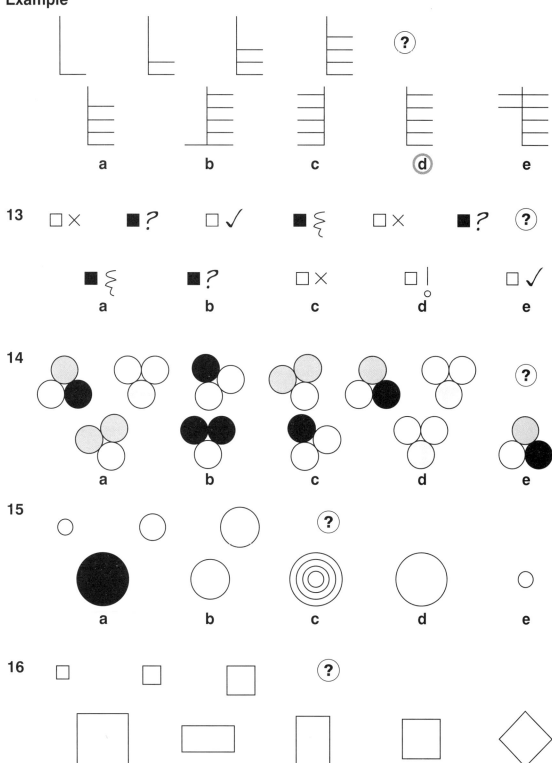

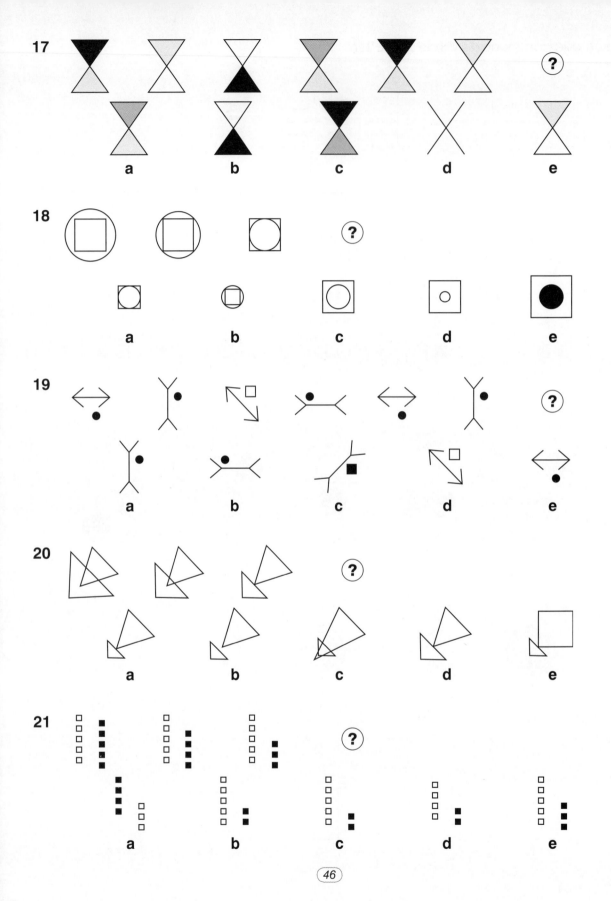

22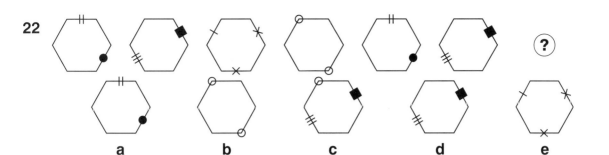

a   b   c   d   e

23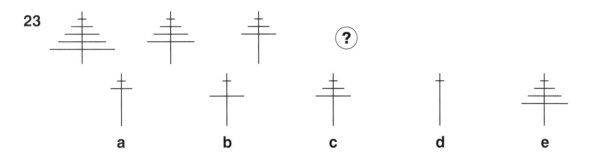

a   b   c   d   e

24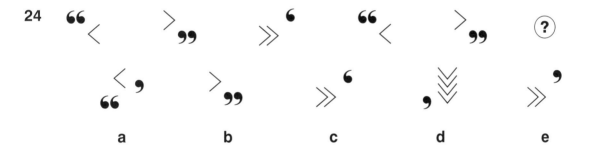

a   b   c   d   e

Which picture completes the second pair in the same way as the first pair?
Circle the letter.

Example

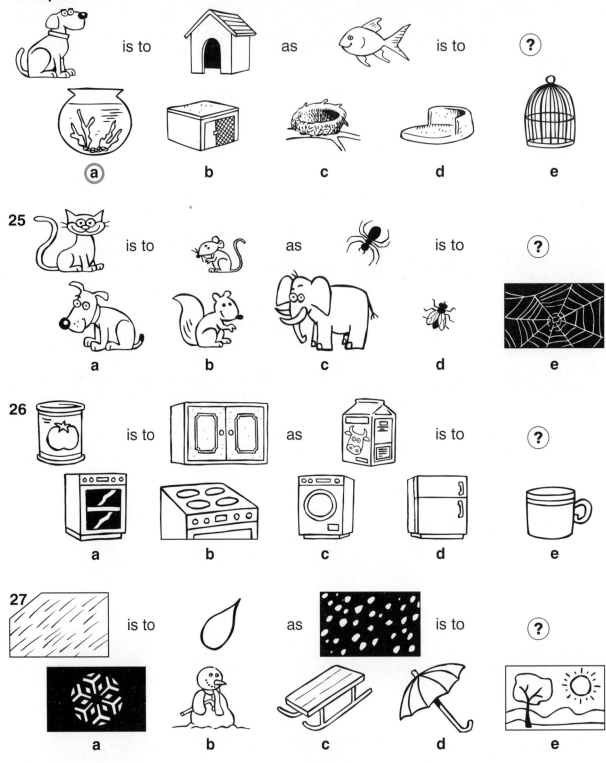

is to ... as ... is to ... ?

a (circled) b c d e

25 is to ... as ... is to ... ?

a b c d e

26 is to ... as ... is to ... ?

a b c d e

27 is to ... as ... is to ... ?

a b c d e

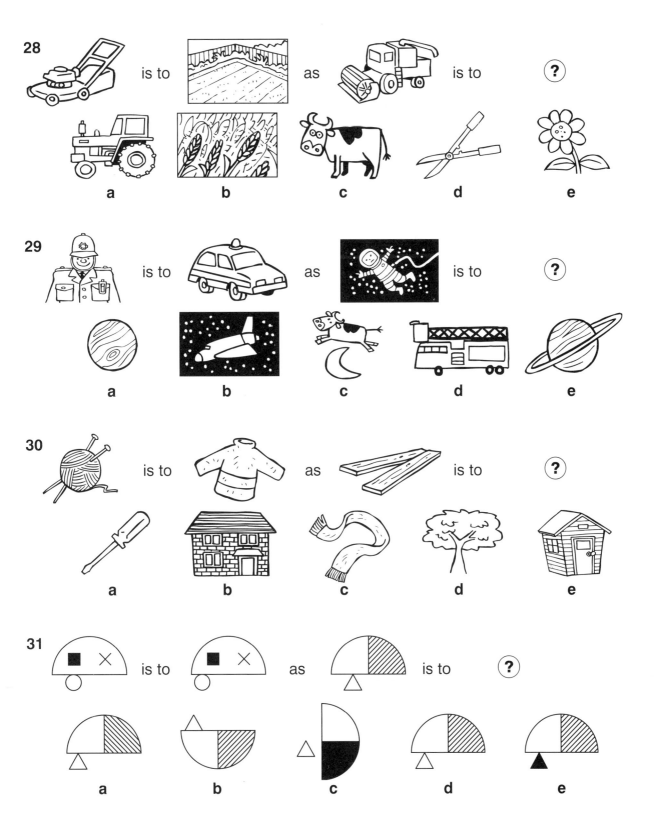

28 is to as is to ?

a b c d e

29 is to as is to ?

a b c d e

30 is to as is to ?

a b c d e

31 is to as is to ?

a b c d e

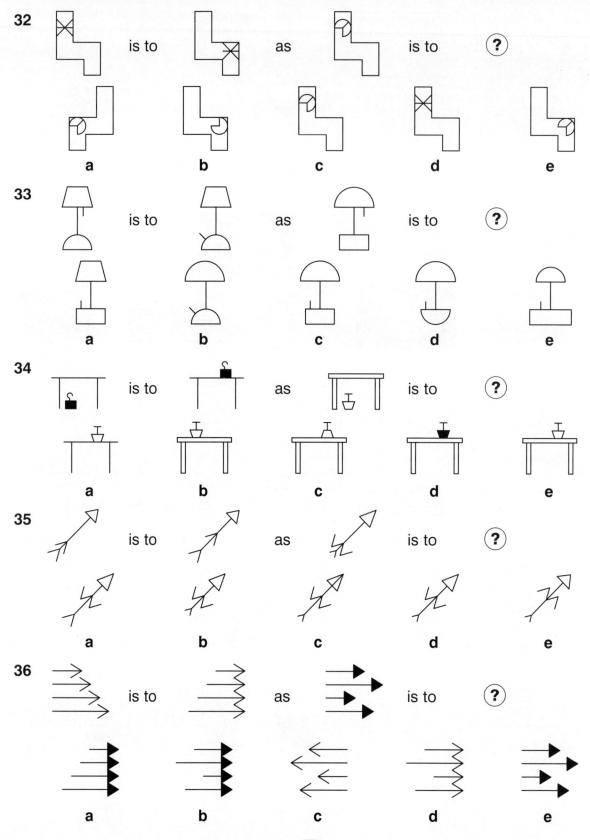

In which larger shape is the shape on the left hidden? Circle the letter.

Example

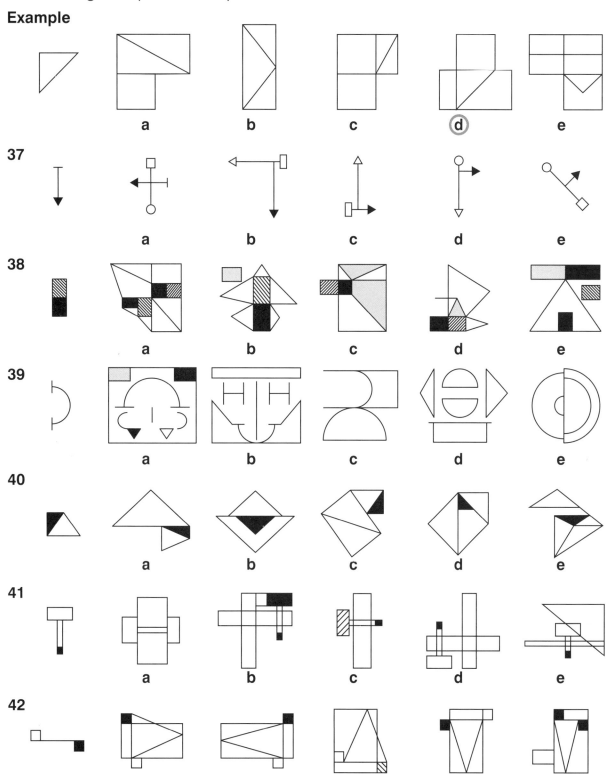

Which shape on the right is the reflection of the shape given on the left?
Circle the letter.

Example

a   b   c   (d)   e

43

a   b   c   d   e

44

a   b   c   d   e

45

a   b   c   d   e

46

a   b   c   d   e

47

a   b   c   d   e

48

a   b   c   d   e

Paper 6

Which is the odd one out? Circle the letter.

Example

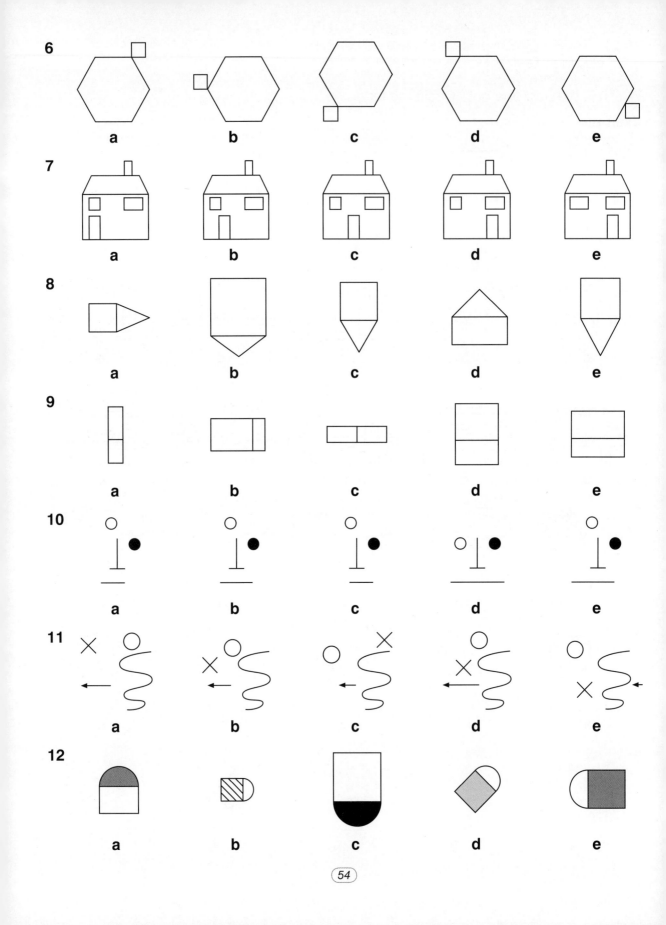

Which one comes next? Circle the letter.

Example

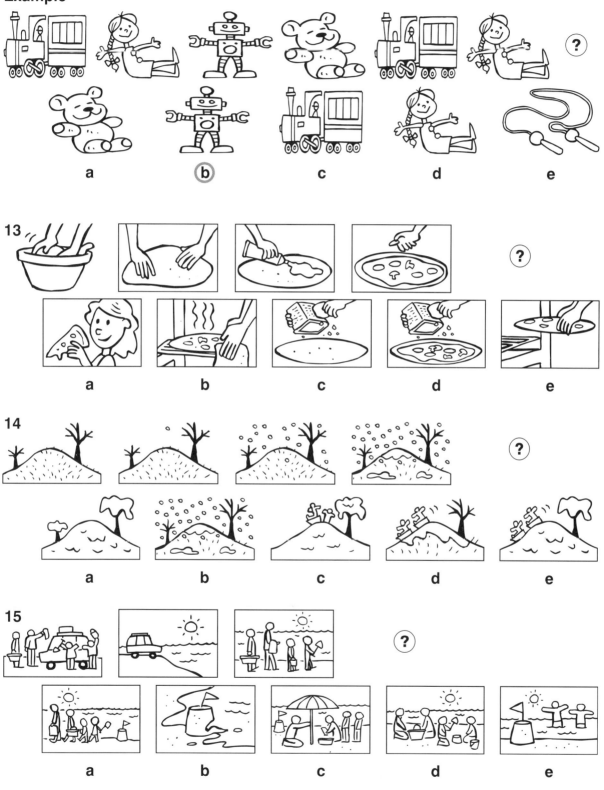

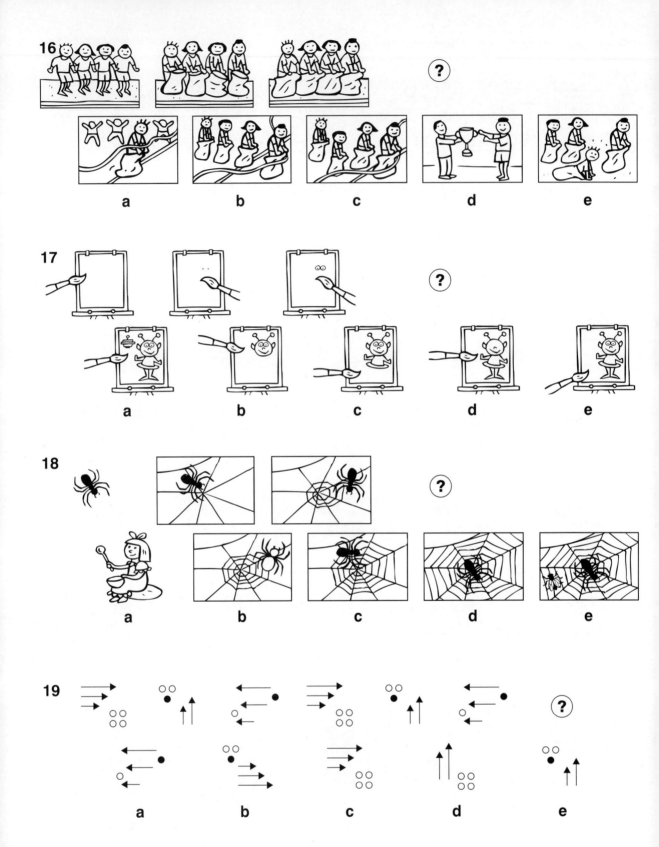

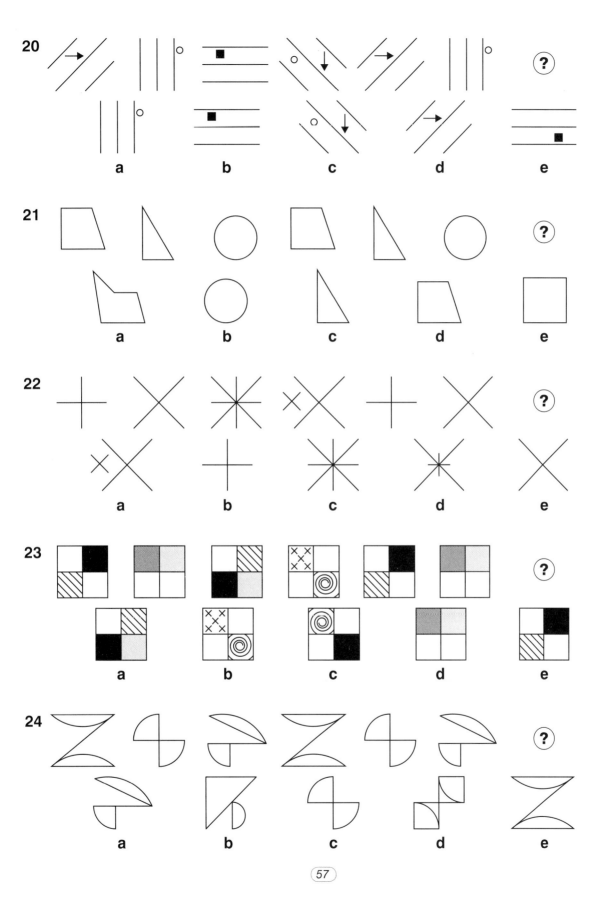

20

a   b   c   d   e

21

a   b   c   d   e

22

a   b   c   d   e

23

a   b   c   d   e

24

a   b   c   d   e

Which picture completes the second pair in the same way as the first pair?
Circle the letter.

Example

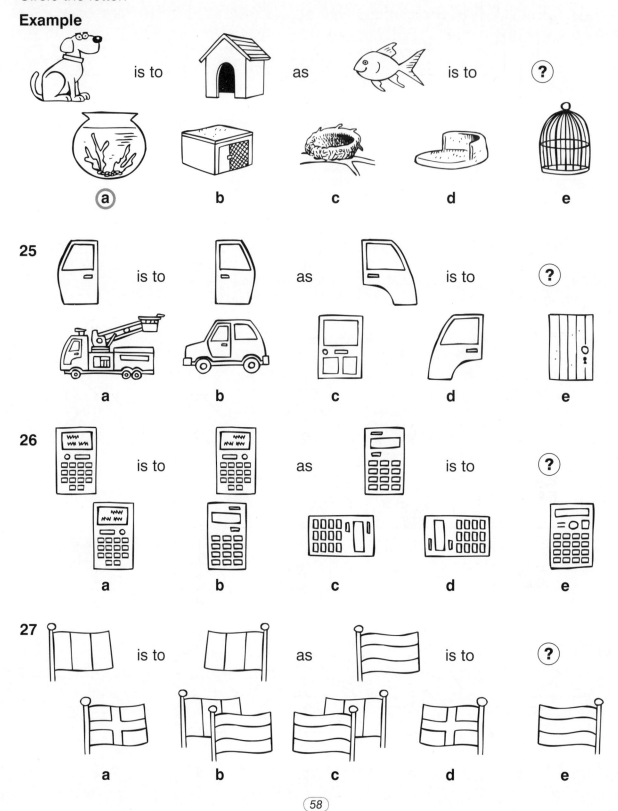

58

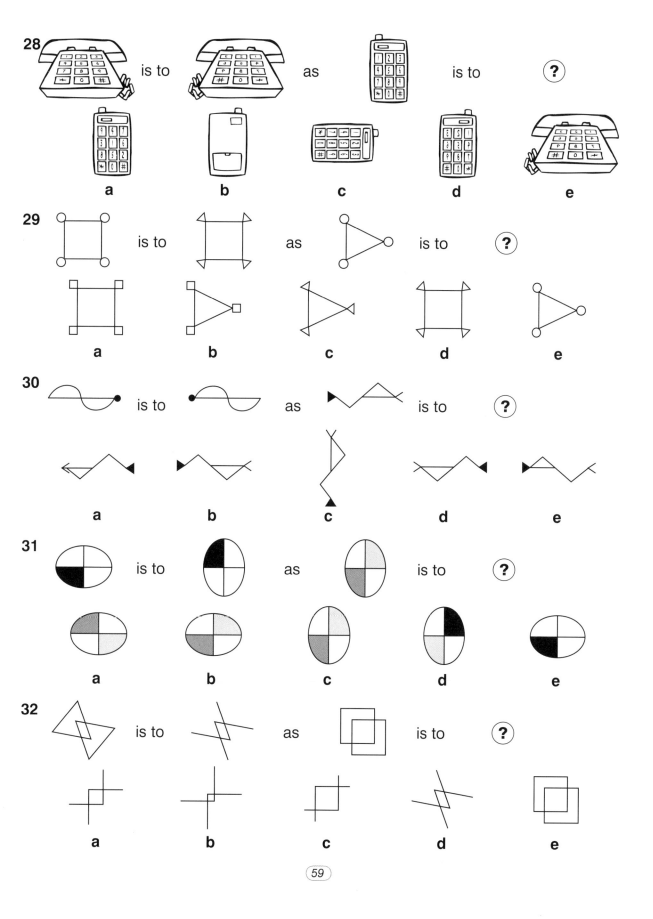

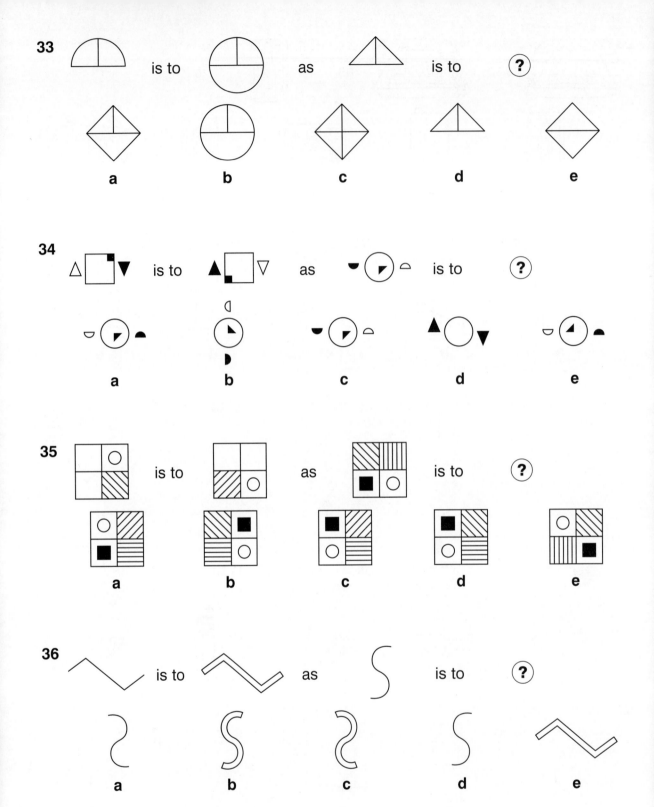

Which shape or pattern completes the larger square? Circle the letter.

Example

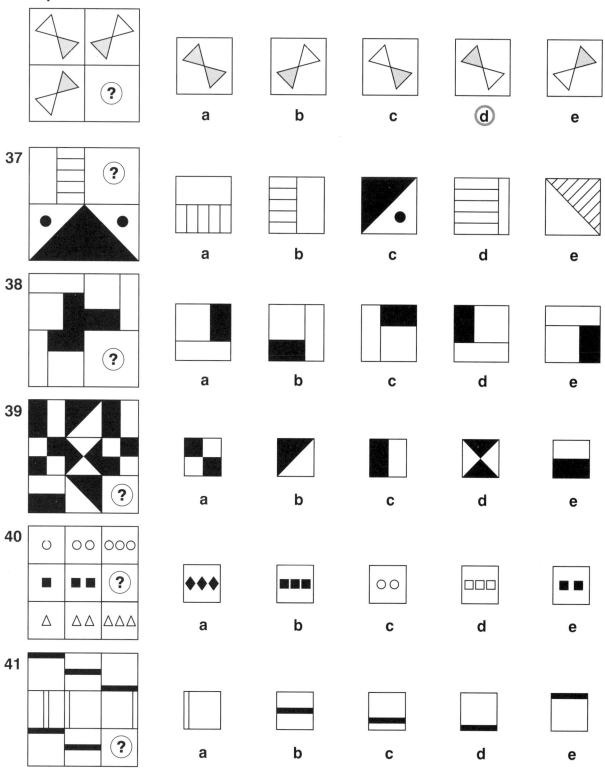

42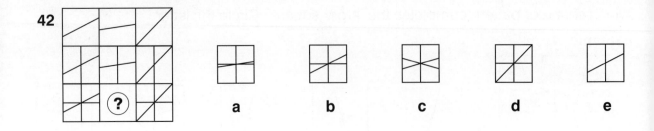

Which code matches the shape or pattern given at the end of each line?
Circle the letter.

Example

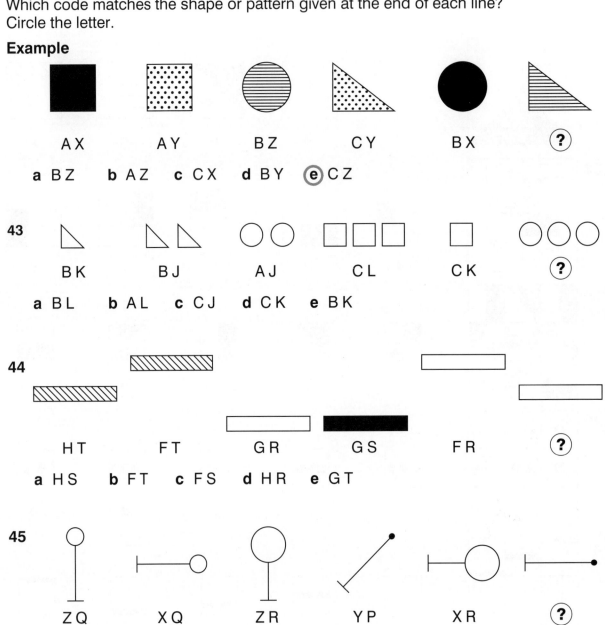

AX   AY   BZ   CY   BX   **?**

a BZ   **b** AZ   **c** CX   **d** BY   **e** CZ

43

BK   BJ   AJ   CL   CK   **?**

a BL   **b** AL   **c** CJ   **d** CK   **e** BK

44

HT   FT   GR   GS   FR   **?**

a HS   **b** FT   **c** FS   **d** HR   **e** GT

45

ZQ   XQ   ZR   YP   XR   **?**

a YR   **b** ZP   **c** XQ   **d** YQ   **e** XP

46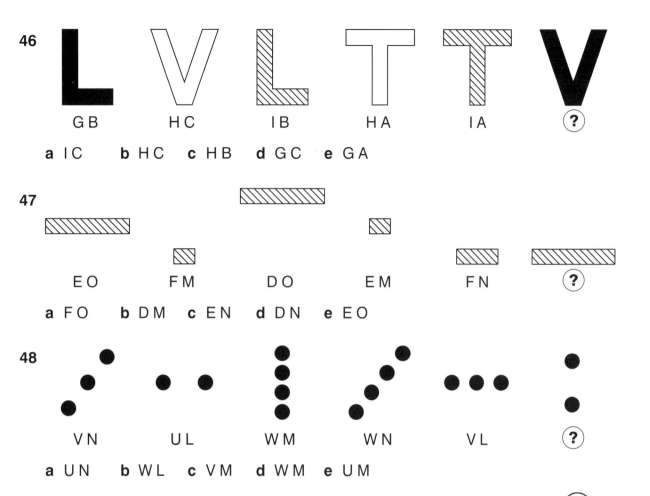

GB   HC   IB   HA   IA   **?**

a IC   **b** HC   **c** HB   **d** GC   **e** GA

47

EO   FM   DO   EM   FN   **?**

a FO   **b** DM   **c** EN   **d** DN   **e** EO

48

VN   UL   WM   WN   VL   **?**

a UN   **b** WL   **c** VM   **d** WM   **e** UM

Now go to the Progress Chart to record your score!   Total ◯ 48

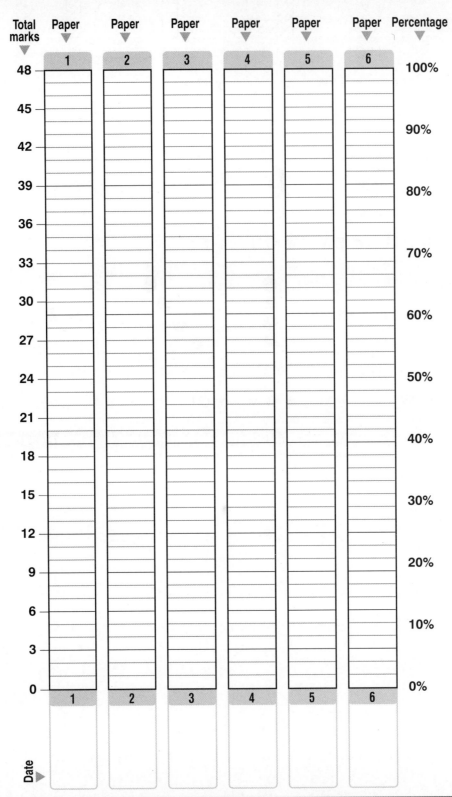